the ULTIMATE
African Heritage
QUIZ
BOOK

Maritime Edition

Craig Marshall Smith

W9-DCF-809

NIMBUS
PUBLISHING

Nimbus Publishing Limited, PO Box 9166, Halifax, NS B3K 5M8 (902) 455-4286, www.nimbus.ca

Printed and bound in Canada
Nimbus Publishing is committed to protecting our natural environment. As part of our efforts, this book is printed on 100% recycled content, Enviro 100.

Author photo: Halifax Public Library

Library and Archives Canada Cataloguing in Publication

Smith, Craig M., 1961-
The ultimate African heritage quiz book /
Craig Marshall Smith. —Maritime ed.
Includes bibliographical references.
ISBN 978-1-55109-683-4
1. Black Canadians—Nova Scotia—Miscellanea—Juvenile literature. 2. Black Canadians—Miscellanea—Juvenile literature.
I. Title.
FC2350.B6S54 2008   j971.6'00496   C2008-904610-2

We acknowledge the financial support of the Government of Canada through the Book Publishing Industry Development Program (BPIDP) and the Canada Council, and of the Province of Nova Scotia through the Department of Tourism, Culture and Heritage for our publishing activities.

This book is dedicated to my family, and to my mother,

brothers, and sister for their unwavering support. It is also

dedicated to the memory of my late father, Bobby Smith.

Table of Contents

Organizations, Politics, and Social Justice

1. Name the French Code by which settlers were allowed to keep black slaves on Île St.-Jean, present-day Prince Edward Island, in 1719.

2. Name the organization founded in New Brunswick in 1959 by Walter Peters, Fred Hodges, Joe Drummond, Garfield Skinner, and Ovid Machett.

3. What is the name of the committee created by Nova Scotia Community College in 2000 as a means of reaching out to the African Nova Scotian community?

4. This man travelled to England to personally petition the British government to live up to the promises it made to black people in Nova Scotia and New Brunswick, and became a leader in both provinces' black communities. What is his name?

5. This woman is known as "the mother of the American Civil Rights Movement." In August 1998, Mount Saint Vincent University in Halifax, Nova Scotia, bestowed an honorary degree upon her. What is her name?

6. In 1991, the Halifax-based Concerned Citizens Against Drugs group held a community conference called "Opportunity to Grow." Their keynote speaker (pictured below) was an American civil rights leader and a founder of the Southern Christian Leadership Conference. What is his name?

7. This Wolfville, Nova Scotia, native was instrumental in the founding of the Nova Scotia Association for the Advancement of Coloured People, the Black United Front, and the Black Cultural Centre. He was also the first black Nova Scotian to hold two university degrees. What is his name?

8. In 1955, this Sydney, Cape Breton, native was elected to the Sydney city council. He was also the first black alderman to be elected in Atlantic Canada. What is his name?

9. During the 1960s, this man was considered one of the most feared people in Canada. He was referred to as the Stockley Carmichael of Canada and was spied on by the RCMP. What is his name?

10. What is the name of the noted African American organizer of the United Negro Improvement Association who visited Halifax and Sydney, Nova Scotia, in 1928?

11. Name the transplanted African Nova Scotian who served as the president of the Nova Scotia Association for the Advancement of Coloured People, co-founder of the Nova Scotia Civil Liberties Association, founder of the Black Educators Association, and member of the board of directors of the Black United Front.

12. Name the New Glasgow, Nova Scotia, native that was once the highest-serving public servant in Canada and went on to represent Canada in Trinidad and Tobago as High Commissioner from 1985 to 1988.

13. Name the member of the Legislative Assembly of Nova Scotia who stated publicly in 2007 that the legislature is brimming with subtle racism.

14. Name the man who was the first African Canadian to be vice-president of a national political party (Progressive Conservative) and was the first African Nova Scotian appointed to the Canadian Senate.

15. In 1984, this descendant of Rose Fortune became the first black female mayor in Canada. She served as mayor of Annapolis Royal from 1984 to 1988 and is now the principal of the Halifax campus of Nova Scotia Community College. What is her name?

16. In 1966, this man won the Canadian Junior Lightweight Championship; in 1990, he was appointed Sergeant-at-Arms for the Nova Scotia House of the Legislative Assembly and became the first black Canadian to be appointed to this post. What is his name?

17. In 2007, the first black Citizenship Court judge for Atlantic Canada was appointed. The woman who received this appointment, pictured below (back row, centre), is a former Nova Scotia Mass Choir member and a former model for the Simpsons-Sears catalogue. What is her name?

18. Name the former director of the Nova Scotia Human Rights Commission who publicly criticized the province of Nova Scotia in 2004 for its lack of racial diversity in a tourism campaign.

19. Name the African Nova Scotian who was appointed ombudsman for the province of Manitoba.

20. Name the African Nova Scotian alderman of Halifax's Ward Three who was the longest-serving alderman in the province.

21. Born and raised in Halifax, Nova Scotia, this man became the first black person elected to the Nova Scotia Legislative Assembly in 1993. He was also the first black Nova Scotian to serve as a provincial cabinet minister. What is his name?

22. This office devoted to the Nova Scotian black community's concerns was created by the provincial government following the 2003 provincial election and it became the first of its kind in Canada. What is the name of the office?

23. Name the grassroots organization that was founded in 1969 with a mandate to bring about positive change for black Nova Scotian learners.

24. Before turning to law, the woman pictured below was a math teacher. On June 1, 2007, she became the first and only Judge of the Tax Court of Canada to be of colour. What is her name?

25. Name the organization founded in 1990 with a mission to establish a support system for working African Nova Scotian artists.

26. Black men have been active in Masonic lodges throughout Nova Scotia. Name the lodge the gentlemen pictured below represent.

27. Name the Nova Scotian government organization that celebrated ten years of serving the African Nova Scotian business community in 2007.

28. Who was the founder and driving force behind the Halifax Coloured Citizens Improvement League?

29. This Nova Scotian institution opened its doors in 1921. Although its reason for existence was to provide a home for orphaned black children, its doors have always been open to children of all races. This organization was also the subject of a book called *Share and Care* by Charles Saunders. What is the name of the organization?

30. This financial institution was founded in East Preston, Nova Scotia, by Ross Kinney and Noel Johnston, and it is named for one of the most famous African American inventors. What is it called?

31. This gathering place was created as a means of involving black youths in politics in the 1960s. Its founders were Rocky and Joan Jones. What is it called?

32. Name the national organization that came under fire in 1994 when reports revealed that it had spied on the black community in Nova Scotia during the 1960s.

33. When Viola Desmond (pictured left) was arrested at the Roseland Theatre in New Glasgow, Nova Scotia, for violating racially discriminatory laws, this organization took the case to the Supreme Court of Canada. What is the name of the organization?

34. This is the only African Canadian society to have an officially registered coat of arms, which was signed by the Right Honourable Michaëlle Jean, Governor General of Canada, on February 12, 2007. What is the name of the society?

35. Name the voluntary non-profit organization that is dedicated to improving the welfare of black Nova Scotian women and their families in their communities.

36. What event occurred in Weaver Settlement, Digby County, Nova Scotia, in 1985, triggering the black community to organize marches in Weymouth Falls?

37. Name the Saint John, New Brunswick, native who founded the Colour Progressive Association; Provincial Resources of Black Energy; Pride of Race, Unity, Dignity, Education (PRUDE); and the Black Loyalists of New Brunswick Association.

38. Name the African Nova Scotian who is the founder of the Run Against Racism.

THE ULTIMATE AFRICAN HERITAGE QUIZ BOOK

39. This Whitney Pier native (pictured left) is the first and only African Nova Scotian to serve as Lieutenant-Governor of Nova Scotia. She has also served as the director of the Nova Scotia Human Rights Commission and as the ombudsman for the province. What is her name?

40. Name the African Nova Scotian community group that staged marches to Province House in Halifax in 2006 to protest the placement of a dump in their community.

41. Name the North Preston native and heavyweight boxing contender that the Nova Scotia Human Rights Commission ruled was discriminated against by the Halifax Regional Police in 2003.

42. **What are the names of the two African Nova Scotian women pictured below selling a ticket for a Halifax Coloured Citizens Improvement League charity event to former African American boxing great Jersey Joe Walcott?**

Sports

1. This African Nova Scotian firefighter represented Nova Scotia at the Scott Firefighter Combat Challenge in Las Vegas, Nevada, in 2007, and finished second in his age category. What is his name?

2. In 1964, this African Nova Scotian woman won the team trophy at a track and field meet held at Mount Allison University in Sackville, New Brunswick. She was the sole representative from her school and placed first in every event. What is her name?

3. This outstanding individual from Halifax, Nova Scotia, was the first black athlete to win a world title in any sport. What is his name?

4. Name the African Nova Scotian reliever who was named rookie of the year in the semi-pro Western Major Baseball league in 2007.

5. This African Nova Scotian was a player and coach in the Newfoundland Senior Hockey League and coached his team to five league championships. In 1985, he was named the best import player to ever come to Newfoundland. What is his name?

6. When this Fredericton, New Brunswick, native took to the ice in 1958 as a player with the Boston Bruins, he became the first black player in the NHL. In 2007, he was the guest of honour at the annual Black Hockey & Sports Hall of Fame induction conference. What is his name?

7. This Softball Canada inductee started out playing baseball on the Halifax Common. In his teenage years he made the switch to softball. He has won three Pan American gold medals as a player and one as a coach and he can throw a softball 109 mph (175 km/h). What is his name?

8. This African Nova Scotian was a member of the 1973 Grey Cup-winning Ottawa Rough Riders. He was the first African Nova Scotian to play in the CFL and the first Canadian to play in the CFL without first playing university football. What is his name?

9. This man has travelled all over Canada calling balls and strikes in his job as a softball umpire. He is also a member of the Softball Canada Hall of Fame, along with his son. What is his name?

10. Who is the African Nova Scotian from Whitney Pier, Cape Breton, whose desire to play baseball took him to the big leagues, where he played for the St. Louis Cardinals?

11. Between the years 1999 and 2001, this African Nova Scotian swimmer collected thirty-six individual age-group records and was named the top female at every meet she attended during that time. What is her name?

12. Name the African Nova Scotian woman pictured below who wrestled under the name Candy Jones in the 1950s.

13. Drafted by the Phoenix Cardinals of the NFL in 1992, this Nova Scotia native has won two Super Bowls with the Dallas Cowboys, a Grey Cup with the Toronto Argonauts, and a Vanier Cup with the Western Mustangs. What is his name?

14. This African Nova Scotian represented his country at the Olympic Games in Montreal in 1976, officiating the women's bronze-medal volleyball game. What is his name?

15. There were two African Nova Scotians signed by the Halifax Rainmen (a professional basketball team) in 2007. One was a former university star, while the other was signed right out of high school. What are their names?

16. At the 1968 Olympic Games in Mexico City, this African Nova Scotian runner was Canada's fastest woman and she was also recognized among the top three runners in the world. What is her name?

17. Name the four African Nova Scotians in the picture below who were members of the 1969 Nova Scotia softball team in the Canada Games.

18. Name the African Nova Scotian senior baseball coach who is a nationally certified softball umpire and a regular co-host on *Harv's Sportsland*, and who tried out for the Boston Red Sox in 1972.

19. On the eve of the new millennium, these four African Nova Scotian sports legends were named in a list of the top ten athletes of the twentieth century. Name the athletes and the sports they represent.

20. This native of Truro, Nova Scotia, was the first African Canadian player in the Newfoundland Senior Hockey League. He also operated a dry cleaning business and a taxi service. What is his name?

21. This African Nova Scotian wrestler from the area known as Sandhill in Amherst thrilled audiences the world over. His son followed in his footsteps, becoming a world-famous wrestler before turning his talents to acting. What is the father's name?

22. Name five members of the 1946 Halifax Rangers senior men's softball team (pictured below).

HALIFAX RANGERS SENIOR SOFTBALL TEAM
1946

23. This man came from a proud family of boxers (his father was a Canadian champion) and he was the first African Nova Scotian boxer to win an Olympic medal. What is his name?

24. This Amherst native coached the Moncton Gagnon Beavers of the Maritime Junior "A" Hockey League and the Moncton Wildcats of the Quebec Major Junior Hockey League. He was also the first African Nova Scotian to play in the NHL. What is his name?

25. Name the Truro native who was the first African Nova Scotian to play professional hockey.

26. This is the oldest continually running all-black basketball tournament in Canada. It was founded in Halifax in 1974. What is it called?

27. Name the members of the first all-black line in professional hockey, pictured below, one of whom was from New Brunswick.

28. Name the all-black hockey league created in Nova Scotia that existed from 1895 to 1925.

29. Name the African American former heavyweight champion who visited Halifax in the late 1950s as a guest wrestling referee.

30. This black Islander set a New Brunswick provincial long-distance speed skating record on April 10, 1892, covering eighteen miles (twenty-nine kilometres) in fifty minutes. He was also the only black member of the famous West End Rangers hockey team. What is his name?

31. What historic event took place in an Atlantic Colleges Athletic Association basketball game in November 2005, as the Mount St. Vincent Mystics took on the St. Thomas Tommies?

32. This Guysborough, Nova Scotia, native raced in the 2008 Boston Marathon, running the last ten kilometres with a leg injury. What is her name?

Education, Literature, and Journalism

1. This individual was the only African Nova Scotian woman to study engineering at Dalhousie University in 2008. She was featured in both the *Chronicle Herald* and the *Daily News*. What is her name?

2. This academic educator has a master of social work degree from Dalhousie University and a doctoral degree in sociological studies from Sheffield University in England. In 2000, she became an associate professor at Dalhousie University. What is her name?

3. This New Glasgow, Nova Scotia, native is the director of the Pre-Service Teacher Program for NASA. She is also the only Canadian to receive a White House Millennium Award for her work in international education. What is her name?

4. In 1994, the BLAC Report created the blueprint for addressing the inadequacies facing African Nova Scotian learners. Name the division within the Nova Scotia Department of Education that was formed as a result of the report's findings.

5. This educator (pictured below, right) was the first and only African Nova Scotian industrial arts teacher. He travelled to schools throughout Halifax County to administer industrial arts in his "shop mobile." What is his name?

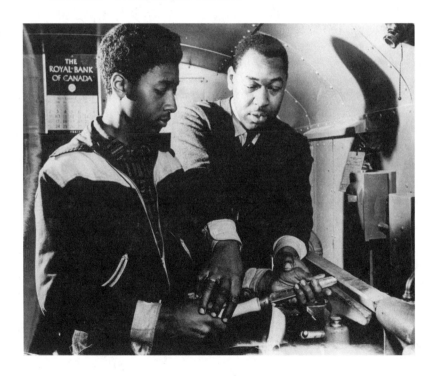

6. This man left his home in Halifax to pursue a career in bricklaying in Boston. From there, he went on to become a minister and a professor, and in 1893 he became the first and only black Nova Scotian to hold the position of president of a college: Livingstone College in Salisbury, North Carolina. What is his name?

7. This woman was born on February 5, 1905, in New Brunswick. Her dream to become an educator took her to Truro, Nova Scotia, where, in 1928, she became the first black person to graduate from the Nova Scotia Provincial Normal College. What is her name?

8. This winner of the Montgomery-Campbell prize was the first African Canadian to graduate from the University of New Brunswick. She graduated with honours and was called "the classical genius of 1905." What is her name?

9. What was the name of the Halifax school erected on Albermarle Street (now Market Street) in January 1836?

10. The Endowed Chair in Black Canadian Studies at Dalhousie University is named for which African Nova Scotian?

11. This man was the first black person to graduate from the New Brunswick Provincial Normal College. He began his teaching career in 1886 at Elm Hill, which was the black settlement on Otnabog Lake. What is his name?

12. Released in 2005 and written by the subject's great-great-grandnephew, Justin Marcus Johnston, this book is about Nova Scotia's first black lawyer. What is the book's title?

13. Released in 2006, this book was edited by Dr. Wanda Thomas Bernard and details the story of a group of black professionals who broke down barriers and fought for change in their everyday work. What is the book's title?

14. Name the book written by Charles Saunders that was a testament to the dedication and commitment of one African Nova Scotian institution that has withstood the test of time.

15. This book of poetry by David Woods also features original paintings by a founder of the Cultural Awareness Youth Group of Nova Scotia. What is the book's title?

16. RCMP Cpl. Craig M. Smith received national attention for his 2006 book on the history of black RCMP members. What is the book's title?

17. Name the book penned by journalist Charles Saunders that is a collection of African Nova Scotian newspaper articles and clippings.

18. Which New Brunswick-born African Canadian was the inspiration for the book *Whistling Banjoman* by Anne Fawcett?

19. This Dartmouth, Nova Scotia, poet won critical acclaim for her book *Borrowed Beauty*. She is also the first African Nova Scotian to serve on the board of governors for Dalhousie University. What is her name?

20. Dawn Williams is an African Canadian author who was born in Britain and now resides in Ontario. In 2002, she published a groundbreaking resource that features over sixty black Maritimers. What is the book's title?

21. In 1893, world-famous Nova Scotian boxing champion George Dixon published an autobiography (pictured right). What is the book's title?

BY

GEORGE DIXON,

CHAMPION FEATHER-WEIGHT OF THE WORLD.

PRICE, - - - 25 CENTS.

22. Who wrote the book *Song of the Spirit: An Historical Narrative On the History of the Beechville United Baptist Church* to commemorate the church's 150th anniversary?

23. Who is the African Nova Scotian that oversaw the development of the BLAC Report and went on to serve as the first director of the African Canadian Services Division of the Nova Scotia Department of Education?

24. The East Preston Baptist Church released a book entitled *Reflections*, celebrating 150 years of worship. The book was edited by Dr. Carolyn G. Thomas. What year was it released?

25. Who wrote the book *The Blacks in New Brunswick*?

26. In what year did former Canadian boxing champion Ricky Anderson release the book *Win in the Arena of Life: Living a Life You Love is Worth Fighting For*?

27. Name the author of *Beneath the Clouds of the Promised Land*, which was published by the Black Educators Association of Nova Scotia.

28. Name the author of the book *Colored Zion*, which is a history of the Zion United Baptist Church in Truro, Nova Scotia.

29. Released in 2005, *Halifax Champion: Black Power in Gloves* was written about which African Nova Scotian boxing champion?

30. Released in 2007, this book was written by the Congress of Black Women of Canada to highlight African Nova Scotian women. What is the book's title?

31. Name the book by Dr. Bridglal Pachai and Dr. Henry Bishop that was released in 2006.

32. Name the two-volume collection of books that was published by the Black Cultural Centre of Nova Scotia. The volumes were released in 1987 and 1990, respectively.

33. Prince Edward Island native Jim Hornby wrote a book that tells the story of PEI's black community and its residents. What is the book's title?

34. Name the Nova Scotian newspaper whose aim was to promote interracial understanding and goodwill among Nova Scotians and to raise the level of awareness about the concerns of the black community.

35. Name the scholarship that was established to honour an African Nova Scotian journalist and activist.

36. Name the African Nova Scotian journalist and New Glasgow native who founded the Black Journalist Association of Nova Scotia.

37. Name two of the African Nova Scotians who have been columnists for either the *Daily News* or the *Chronicle Herald*.

38. Which Halifax, Nova Scotia, native was named assistant managing editor for the Halifax *Chronicle Herald* in 1999?

39. Nova Scotia's first black magazine (pictured right) began operation in 1915 and sold for either ten cents monthly or one dollar for a yearly subscription. It was in publication until May 1917. What was the name of the magazine?

Edited by
E. L. CROSS

10c.
MONTHLY

$1.00
PER ANNUM

JANUARY
1917

Vol. 1.

No. 7.

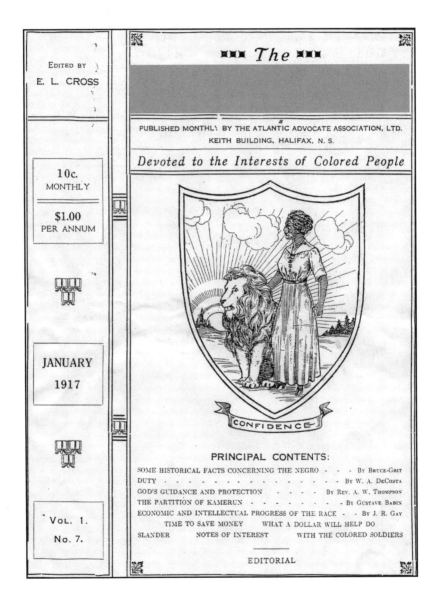

■■■ *The* ■■■

PUBLISHED MONTHLY BY THE ATLANTIC ADVOCATE ASSOCIATION, LTD.
KEITH BUILDING, HALIFAX, N. S.

Devoted to the Interests of Colored People

CONFIDENCE

PRINCIPAL CONTENTS:

40. In 2006, the Council on African Canadian Education (CACE) in conjunction with Mount Saint Vincent University offered a new Master of Education degree program. What is the name of the program?

41. This Nova Scotian newspaper was founded by lawyer Frederick Allan Hamilton in Sydney, Cape Breton, in 1929. The paper aimed at "unifying the coloured people of the Province of Nova Scotia." What was it called?

42. What is the name of the book that caused the black community of Nova Scotia to pressure the Department of Education for its removal from the classrooms in the 1960s?

43. Can you name the African Nova Scotian educator who was thrust into the national spotlight and labelled a segregationist when he suggested the need for an Afrocentric high school in Nova Scotia?

Military, Law, and Justice

1. After seeing RCMP members on motorcycles escorting Queen Elizabeth II, this Saint John, New Brunswick, native told his mother he wanted to be a Mountie. In 1969, he became one of the first black Mounties in Canada. What is his name?

2. There are three African Nova Scotian commissioned officers in the Royal Canadian Mounted Police. Name all three and their ranks, and indicate who was the first to be commissioned.

3. The odds appeared to be against this woman in 1998, but when all of the votes had been counted, she became Nova Scotia's first black female MLA. What is her name?

4. The man pictured left is the longest-serving black auxiliary policeman in Nova Scotia. What is his name?

5. Growing up, she thought of becoming a teacher, but it was a career in law that became her calling. She is the first black provincial court judge in Nova Scotia. What is her name?

6. Name the Shelburne, Nova Scotia, native who was the first black female member of the Royal Canadian Mounted Police to be promoted to the rank of corporal.

7. Name the North Preston native who was the recipient of the Halifax Regional Police Officer of the Year Award in 2007.

8. These two Sydney, Cape Breton, natives were the first two recorded African Canadians to apply to join the Royal Canadian Mounted Police. What are their names?

9. This woman was recognized as the first black female police officer in North America. Her job was to keep the peace on the wharf at Annapolis Royal. What is her name?

10. After protests from African Canadian men who wanted to serve their country, the Canadian military established this black labour unit in Nova Scotia in 1916. Members of this unit served overseas during World War I. What is the name of the unit?

11. This Dartmouth, Nova Scotia, native was the first and highest-ranking black female officer in the Canadian Forces Army Reserve. She spent her reserve time in Ontario. What is her name?

12. Name the No. 2 Construction Battalion member and Yarmouth, Nova Scotia, native whose victory medal was auctioned off on eBay in 2007.

13. This Whitney Pier, Cape Breton, native is the first African Nova Scotian naval reservist. What is her name?

14. This man was born in Horton Bluff, Nova Scotia, in 1826. His father was a slave in the state of Virginia who came to Nova Scotia during the War of 1812. He served in both the British and American navies during his career. In 1857, he received the highest military honour awarded in the British Empire, and was the first Canadian sailor to receive this honour. What is his name?

15. In 2005, as part of the Black Cultural Centre's anniversary dinner, five veterans of World War II were honoured for their help in liberating Normandy. What are their names?

16. Name the African Nova Scotian lawyer who argued before the Supreme Court of Canada on February 25, 2008, to uphold the rights of youths giving statements to the police.

17. What is the name of the former Halifax city police officer pictured below who served thirty years on the force before his retirement?

18. This African Nova Scotian is the only known Black Canadian to serve as a Royal Canadian Air Force aircrew officer. He flew forty-two operational missions in Europe during World War Two. What is his name?

Arts and Culture

1. The African Nova Scotian pictured right followed in his family's musical tradition, which was started a generation before him. He has blown his horn with jazz greats like Louis Armstrong, Dizzie Gillespie, and Oscar Peterson. B. B. King asked him to join his band and tour with him. What is his name?

2. This black Nova Scotian was the first recipient of the Portia White Prize, which is presented for artistic excellence in Nova Scotia. He was also a recipient of the Governor General's Literary Award for poetry for his book *Execution Poems*. What is his name?

3. This man was born in New Glasgow, Nova Scotia, where it was decided that he would be a doctor. After trying his hand at medicine, his love of the theatre won out and, in 1967, he travelled to New York City, where he perfected his craft. In 1972, he returned to Nova Scotia to become the province's first black professional actor. What is his name?

4. This black Nova Scotian's basket making is recognized locally, nationally, and internationally. Today, her daughter carries on the family tradition. Name the woman and her daughter.

5. In 1994, the Beechville, Nova Scotia, filmmaker pictured right won a Canadian Gemini Award and the Japanese Madea Prize for her film *Speak It! From the Heart of Black Nova Scotia*. What is her name?

6. These black Nova Scotians were members of a dance team and were Maritime step-and-tap dance champions. One was from Halifax and the other was from East Green Harbour. What are their names?

7. Name the Cherry Brook native who starred as Mufasa in the Toronto, Ontario, production of the hit musical *The Lion King*.

8. Name the contemporary Canadian opera written by poet and playwright Dr. George Elliott Clarke that aired on CBC-TV in 2001.

9. On April 2, 1999, CBC Radio broadcasted a gospel cantata called "Easter Suite" that featured Woody Woods, the Nova Scotia Mass Choir, Symphony Nova Scotia, and a number of solo artists. Who composed "Easter Suite"?

10. This African Nova Scotian playwright and journalist wrote the acclaimed works *Shine Boy*, *Gideon's Blues*, and *Consecrated Ground*. What is his name?

11. Name the North Preston native who attended the prestigious Berklee College of Music.

12. Name the two African Nova Scotians pictured right who were regularly featured on the CBC show *Singalong Jubilee*.

13. This organization is dedicated to developing, promoting, and enhancing African Nova Scotian music locally, nationally, and internationally. In 2000, it held its first award show. What is the organization called?

14. These two Nova Scotian rappers (pictured below) signed with the major record label Capital/EMI. Their first hit, "So Listen," was aired on MuchMusic. What are their names?

15. Name the African Nova Scotian who was the runner-up on the first season of *Canadian Idol*.

16. The Missionaires were a famous male group from Yarmouth who started singing in 1948. Name the four original members of the group, who are pictured below.

17. Name the members of the Halifax, Nova Scotia, singing group The Raindrops, who recorded the songs "Admit You Done Me Wrong" and "I'm Gonna Cry So Many Tears" in the 1960s.

18. This singer made her international debut in 1944 at the Town Hall in New York City. Later that same year, she began a three-month tour of Latin America on behalf of the Negro Youth Congress. She also performed in London, Paris, and across the United States during her career. What is her name?

19. Name the African Nova Scotian artist from Yarmouth whose work is featured in the Yarmouth County Museum and Archives.

20. This African American actor starred in a weekly sitcom as a single minister with Sherman Hemsley (of *The Jeffersons* fame) as his deacon. He has Nova Scotian roots in Hammonds Plains. What is his name?

21. Edward Kennedy (Duke) Ellington is recognized as one of America's greatest composers. In 1999, Halifax journalist Bruce Nunn uncovered a musical composition written by Duke Ellington and named for an African Nova Scotian woman whom he had made a promise to years earlier. Who was the woman the song was named after?

22. The North Preston native pictured below, who is also a member of the Canadian military, has been playing the bagpipes since the age of twelve. What is his name?

23. Name the African Nova Scotian artist from Weymouth whose work includes the sketch pictured below, *Never Go Fishing Alone*, which is on display at the Art Gallery of Nova Scotia.

Business and Careers

1. Name the African Nova Scotian woman who is the only female cooper (barrel maker) in Canada.

2. Name the businessman who won the Atlantic Canadian Entrepreneur and Manufacturer of the Year award in 1999 for his dispensing equipment.

3. What is the name of the Dartmouth, Nova Scotia, native that started out in the beauty supply industry as a receptionist and went on to become one of the largest distributors of beauty supplies in Canada?

4. Name the Fredericton, New Brunswick, native who operates her own media production company called Mirabliss.

5. Who was the first African Nova Scotian to serve as the executive director of the Better Business Bureau of the Maritime Provinces Inc.?

6. These women were the first two African Canadian graduates of a nursing program in the Maritimes. They graduated from the Children's Hospital in Halifax in 1948. What are their names?

7. Who was the first female executive director of the Black Educators Association?

8. The Black Cultural Centre unveiled the "Wall of Flame" in May 2007 to honour black firefighters in the Halifax region. Who was Halifax's first black firefighter?

9. Name the African Nova Scotian woman pictured below, far right, who was hired to portray Aunt Jemima, one of the most recognized African American icons.

10. This woman was the first black graduate from the Nova Scotia Hospital School of Nursing in Dartmouth, Nova Scotia. She was also the first black person to be elected president of the Registered Nurses Association of Nova Scotia. What is her name?

11. What is the name of the first black associate curator of the Art Gallery of Nova Scotia?

12. This individual is the only African Nova Scotian woman to have ever graduated from the Funeral and Allied Health Services program at the Nova Scotia Community College campus in the Annapolis Valley of Nova Scotia. She is currently the manager of funeral services for T. K. Barnard Funeral Homes Ltd. What is her name?

13. This African Nova Scotian started her career putting away books and participating in puppet shows at the Halifax North Memorial Public Library. In 1984, she became the first African Nova Scotian to graduate from Dalhousie University with a Master of Library Science degree. What is her name?

Religion

1. This place of worship, located in Halifax, has the distinction of being called "the mother church of the African United Baptist Association." What is the name of the church?

2. In what year and in what Nova Scotian location was the African United Baptist Association founded?

3. Who is known as the founder of the African United Baptist Association?

4. In 2002, this woman became the first African Nova Scotian to graduate from the Atlantic School of Theology. What is her name?

5. Who is the first African Canadian woman to be ordained in the United Baptist Convention of the Atlantic Provinces?

6. The ordained minister, African United Baptist Association of Nova Scotia member, and author pictured below was appointed professor of Christian social ethics at Princeton Theological Seminary in New Jersey in 1985. What is his name?

7. This woman was the organist at the Zion Baptist Church in Truro, Nova Scotia, from 1925 to 1997. She is considered one of the longest-serving organists in Nova Scotia. What is her name?

8. This man was the first black Baptist minister in Canada and his pastorship began at the first black Baptist church in Nova Scotia. What is his name?

Achievements

1. This north-end Halifax native was featured in the January 1, 2000, edition of *Maclean's*, where he was called a "Canadian young person to watch." What is his name?

2. This woman devoted her time and efforts to educating people of all ages. She received national recognition from two Governors General for her hard work and dedication. In 1977, Governor General Jules Léger presented her with the Queen's Silver Jubilee Medal, and in 1983, Governor General Edward Schreyer presented her with an Award in Commemoration of the Persons Case. What is her name?

3. This Baptist minister, who was the son of a Virginian slave, became the first black minister to preach at the Baptist convention in Wolfville, Nova Scotia. He was also the only black captain and chaplain in the British Empire during World War I. What is his name?

4. This Cook's Cove, Guysborough County, native was the first black person to graduate from New Glasgow High School in New Glasgow, Nova Scotia. She was also the first female moderator of the African United Baptist Association and the first black woman in Canada to be named "woman of the year" by *Maclean's* magazine. What is her name?

5. When Canada was handing out the first-ever Wazee Awards, this founding member of the Africville Genealogical Society was one of the five recipients. What is her name?

6. This black New Brunswick native was a member of the Canadian military's famed "Snow Birds." He was also a founding member of the New Brunswick Association for the Advancement of Coloured People. What is his name?

7. On October 4, 2003, the first Canadian National Griot Awards were handed out in Edmonton, Alberta. Four African Nova Scotians were among the recipients in the humanitarian, performing arts, sports—youth (swimming), and community service categories. What are the names of the four winners?

8. When the Order of Canada was created in 1967, this man from Sydney, Cape Breton, was the first African Canadian to receive it. What is his name?

9. This Windsor, Nova Scotia, native was recognized in 2007 for her thirty-one-year service as the coordinator of the Cornwallis Street United Baptist Church's hot lunch program. She has been an active member of the Cornwallis Street United Baptist Church for over fifty years. What is her name?

10. This Beechville, Nova Scotia, resident was re-elected to the position of president of the Canadian Association of Social Workers in 2007. She has also served on the board of Big Brother/Big Sisters. What is her name?

Historical Events, Locations, and Places

1. Name the Hollywood star who visited the Nova Scotian black community of North Preston in 2006 while making the film *Poor Boy's Game* in Halifax.

2. What is the name of the Halifax, Nova Scotia, dance hall where legends like Louis Armstrong and Lionel Hampton played in the 1940s and 50s?

3. Established in 1983, this institution is the only museum solely dedicated to the preservation of black history and culture in Nova Scotia. What is the name of the museum?

4. This site of Canada's first race riot was one of the first major African Canadian settlements in Nova Scotia. What is the name of the settlement?

5. In which Nova Scotian city would you find the international and Canadian chapter of the National Association of Buffalo Soldiers and Troopers Motorcycle Club?

6. Name the Maritime provinces that received black residents, either free or slaves, in the 1780s.

7. This African Nova Scotian is recognized as the hero of the Springhill, Nova Scotia, mining disaster of 1958. He has also been highlighted in a made-for-TV Canadian historical vignette. What is his name?

8. Which two African Nova Scotian historical sites were set on fire in early 2007?

9. The Halifax nightclub pictured below was owned and operated by Billy Downey. It opened on Creighton Street in 1962, moved to Agricola Street six months later, relocated to Brunswick Street in 1970, and closed its doors in 1981. During its heyday, it featured such stars as Lots a Papa and Little Anthony and the Imperials. What is the name of the club?

10. Name the African Nova Scotian man who is credited with making the Halifax North Memorial Public Library the focal point of the inner-city community where he grew up.

11. The Trelawney Maroons from Jamaica came to Nova Scotia in 1796. Name the historical site in Halifax that the Maroons helped to reconstruct.

12. A replica of this slave/cargo ship visited Halifax, Nova Scotia, in 2006. The original vessel that this replica was based on was the scene of a revolt and was made famous in a motion picture. What is the name of the ship?

13. What is the name of the community in Sierra Leone that was founded by 1,196 black emigrants from Nova Scotia and New Brunswick in 1792?

14. This annual event has taken place at Seaview Park in Halifax for twenty-four years. In 2007, the event was the target of vandals, who painted racist graffiti on several of the park benches. What is the name of this annual gathering?

15. The presence of the first slave in Canada was recorded in 1628. The slave, a young boy, came to Canada from Madagascar. In 1632, he was baptized and given a name. What is the name that was given to this young boy?

16. There were three names given to the Charlottetown, PEI, bridge that joined Brighton Road and Euston Street; one was Sam's Bridge and another was Samuel Martin's Bridge. What was the third name by which the bridge was commonly known?

17. The Black Cultural Centre in Dartmouth, Nova Scotia, was the site of a historic event on the evening of February 12, 2007, as two of Queen Elizabeth II's representatives in Canada, pictured below, took part in a Black History Month celebration. Name the two representatives who took part and their titles.

18. Name the social club established in Charlottetown, PEI, in the late 1880s by the city's black community.

19. In 1960, the *Globe and Mail* ran an article by Alan MacEachern with the headline "U.S. civil-rights leader was turned away by a resort in New Brunswick." Name the civil rights leader who was the focus of this article.

Common Denominator

For the following questions, guess which profession all of the individuals listed have in common.

1. George Fenton, Harold (Buddy) Parker, John Pannill, Harold Adams, Wayne Bundy, Junior (Burt) Desmond, Arnold Kelly, and Colter States.

2. Walter Skeir, Barry States, Clayton Gannon, Gerald Smith, Nadine Parsons, Theaston Prevost, Milo Adams, Wendell Skeir, Lezlie States, and Thane Smith.

3. Carl Campy Crawford, Milton Williams, Barney Ogden, Don McLean, Tess Viner, Cedric Upshaw, Joel Hussey, Ricky Smith, and Warren Bundy (Adams).

4. Van Roy Tobitt, Patricia Barton, Shawn Mantley, Rowena Jarvis Morrison, Marion Skinner, Janis Jones, Myla Borden, Ken Fells, Ben Elms, and Nolan Borden.

5. George Davis, Shauna Hoyte, Corrine Sparks, Denise Mintis-Smith, Alonzo Wright, Kendrick Douglas, Marcel Prevost, Jean Whalen, Valerie Miller, and Castor Williams.

6. Greenville Flash, Boston Tar Baby, Little Chocolate, Old Chocolate, Ricky Anderson, David Downey, and Tiger Warrington.

7. Sharon Brown (Ross), Paula Fairfax, Tamara Tynes, Althea Reyes, Daisy Grosse Bundy, and Elizabeth McKenna (Hampden).

8. George Francis, Willard P. Clayton, Donald Skeir, Wellington States, Tracy Grosse, Elaine Walcott, and Peter J. Paris.

9. Clinton David, Danny Williams, Freddie Brooks, Charlie Grosse, Lloyd Simmonds, Melvin Carter, Buddy Daye Jr., John Glasgow, Ernest Glasgow, and Derrick Williams.

10. Susan Edmonds, Donna Smith, Ruth Bailey, Gwen Barton, Clotilda Yakimczuk, Martha Borden, and Gussie Ellis.

Name the Date

1. The Preston electoral district includes the three historic black communities of Cherry Brook, East Preston, and North Preston. In what year did the Nova Scotia government create the constituency of Preston?

2. Nova Scotian boxer Sam Langford was known as the "greatest champion that never was." In what year was he inducted into the World Boxing Hall of Fame?

3. The African School in Saint John, New Brunswick, operated by the Madras Board, opened in what month and year?

4. In what year was the Nova Scotia Association for the Advancement of Coloured People formed?

5. In what year did the provincial black social reform organization known as BUF (Black United Front) begin operating?

6. In what year did the Halifax municipal government approve the plan to remove residents from the black community of Africville?

7. In what year did delegates from the Black Panthers visit Halifax?

8. In the 1990s, Dalhousie University hosted the "Black Men Surviving the 90s" conference, which brought together African Nova Scotians and participants from England. In what month and year was this conference held?

9. Between which years did black American slaves escape to the Maritimes via the Underground Railway?

10. In what year did the Black Refugees come to Nova Scotia?

11. In what year did legal segregation of Nova Scotian schools end?

12. Mathieu De Costa, the first recorded black person in what is now known as Nova Scotia, arrived there in what year?

13. In what year did the Halifax North Memorial Public Library begin Black History Month programming?

14. The Upper Hammonds Plains volunteer fire department was the first incorporated black department in Canada. Can you name the year it was incorporated?

15. On what date did Lieutenant-Governor John Ready pass a law that officially abolished slavery on Prince Edward Island?

16. The Cultural Awareness Youth Group of Nova Scotia was an important organization that enabled youths to have a voice in their schools and community. In what year did the youth group come into existence and who was its founder?

17. The first reunion and recognition banquet held to honour World War I veterans of the No. 2 Construction Battalion was held in what year and at what location?

Name the Place

For each of the following questions, name the community, county, region, or province that is home to the families listed.

1. Paris, Clyke, Jones, Mentis, Tynes, Borden, Jackson, Maxwell, Jewell, Jordan, and Armstrong (Community)

2. Borden, MacLean, Paris, Dorrington, Reddick, Desmond, Gero, Elms, and Jewell (Community)

3. Ruck, Desmond, Skeete, Green, Streete, Talbot, Alleyne, Paris, Best, Jones, Bryan, Worrell, Moe, Crawford, and Coward (Region)

4. Cromwell, Jarvis, Langford, Bishop, Pleasant, Bright, and Middleton (County)

5. Crawford, Fells, Lawrence, Fowler, Johnson, Falls, Smith, Anderson, Francis, Ogden, Sykes, Munro, and Stevenson (County)

6. Cain, Brooks, Williams, Sparks, Clayton, Fraser, Thomas, Riley, Downey, Grosse, Fairfax, Beals, Glasgow, Drummond, and Slawter (County)

7. Cook, Halfkenny, Bowles, Sylvie, Gabriel, Reid, Lee, and Jones (County)

8. Steed, Dixon, Flint, Carvery, Izzard, Howe, Mantley, and Grant (Community)

9. Miller, Francis, Barton, Jordan, Bright, Robinson, Simms, Elms, Guy, and Cromwell (County)

10. Stevens, Farmer, Guy, Hartley, and Herbert (Community)

11. Drummond, White, Peters, Skinner, Stevenson, Miller, Brown, McIntyre, Roach, Sheppard, Hogan, Hynes, Hector, Patterson, Dixon, Brothers, Hodges, Hollmes, Stevens, Palmer, Simpson, Thompson, Edison, Thomas, Bree, Tyler, Richards, Scott, and Smith (Community)

12. O' Ree, Hudlin, McIntyre, Nash, McCarty, Carty, Howe, Eatmon/Eatman, Jones, Young, Diamond/ Dyamond, Claybourne, McCarthy, Hoyt, Lawrence, and McCain (Community)

13. Davis, Johnston, Skeir, Smith, Downey, Loppie, Johnson, Brown, Gannon, Chandler, Daye, Adams, Patterson, Earle, White, and Prevost (Community)

14. Ryan, Byers, Godfrey, and Mills (Province)

African Canadian Icons

1. This African Canadian was a member of Canada's national women's hockey team for ten years, winning four world titles and MVP recognitions along the way. What is her name?

2. Originally from South Carolina, this man settled near Calgary, Alberta, during the 1880s. He became a respected cattleman and was well known for his ability to break horses. What is his name?

3. This African Canadian inventor was born in Colchester, Ontario. He registered forty-two patents in his lifetime. It is said that the phrase "the real McCoy" was created because of him. What is his name?

4. His photos of the Swan River Valley in Manitoba proved to be geographical masterpieces that are still used today. What is his name?

5. In 1868, this African Canadian, who had lived in both the United States and Canada, was a representative at the Yale Convention, where the terms were laid to allow British Columbia to join Confederation. What is his name?

6. This African Canadian from North Battleford, Saskatchewan, was named the NFL's offensive rookie of the year in 1986. He was also a star player for the Washington State University Cougars, where he was an All-American athlete. What is his name?

7. Only two African Canadians have had a postage stamp printed in their honour by Canada Post. Both are from the world of music, and one was the first living Canadian to be so honoured. What are their names and which one was the first living Canadian to be so honoured?

8. Name the African Canadian slave who helped raise awareness of the brutality facing slaves in Canada with her public execution by hanging in Montreal.

Who am I?

1. • I am a community activist from New Glasgow, Nova Scotia.
   • I had a radio show called *The Quiet Corner*.
   • I wrote and published my autobiography, *The Lonesome Road*, in 1977.
   • I received an honorary degree from St. Francis Xavier University.
   • I am a member of the Order of Canada.
   Who am I?

2. • I was born in Sackville, New Brunswick, in 1876.
   • I became the first black artist to win a national art prize in North America.
   • In 2007, the Art Gallery of Nova Scotia purchased and unveiled one my paintings, *River Scene*, (pictured right).
   • I was instrumental in establishing the Providence Art Club, which later became the Rhode Island School of Design.
   Who am I?

3. • I am known as "Mr. Baseball" in my home province of Prince Edward Island.

• I served my country as part of the 21st Field Ambulance Medical Corps during World War II.

• I was the first black Islander to hold the position of recreation director in the province.

• In 1986, I was inducted into the Prince Edward Island Sport Hall of Fame.

Who am I?

4. • I was born and raised in Halifax, where I graduated from King's College with a bachelor of arts degree in 1963.

   • In 1971, I was promoted to chief human rights officer for Nova Scotia.

   • In 1982, I was appointed provincial ombudsman for the province of Manitoba.

   • In 1997, I became Nova Scotia's first black member of Parliament and served as the New Democratic Party's spokesperson for National Defence, Veterans' Affairs, and Multiculturalism.

   Who am I?

5. • I hold a Bachelor of Music Degree from the University of Toronto.

   • In 1998, I played the lead role in the opera *Beatrice Chancey* by James Rolfe and Dr. George Elliott Clarke.

   • In 2002, I won the Jeunesses Musicales Montréal International Competition.

   • In 2004, I made my American debut at the world-famous Carnegie Hall.

   • I accompanied Governor General Adrienne Clarkson on her official trip to Russia.

   Who am I?

6. • Before turning thirty, I was one of the founding members and performers of Word Iz Bond, a spoken word artist collective.

   • I have performed nationally and internationally.

   • I have directed and composed for the Nova Scotia Mass Choir for five years.

   • I was a featured conductor on the national six-part series *Gospel Challenge* on Vision TV, and I am the host of *All the Best*, a regional CBC Radio music program.

   • I have a Bachelor of Music degree from Dalhousie University and a Bachelor of Journalism degree from the University of King's College.

   • I am pictured below.

   Who am I?

7. • I was taught how to box by a fellow Islander, the great George "Old Chocolate" Godfrey.

   • In 1897, I knocked out Harry Peppers of California to win the Colored Middleweight Title.

   • Boxing legend Sam Langford credited me with teaching him everything he knew about boxing.

   • Following my boxing career, I worked for the B & M railroad for nearly twenty years.

   • I am pictured right.

   Who am I?

Answers

Organizations, Politics, and Social Justice

1. Code Noir or Black Code
2. New Brunswick Association for the Advancement of Coloured People
3. Nova Scotia Community College African Nova Scotian Advisory Committee
4. Thomas Peters
5. Rosa Parks
6. Rev. Dr. Joseph Lowery
7. Rev. Dr. William P. Oliver, OC
8. Tom Miller Sr.
9. Burnley Rocky Jones
10. Marcus Garvey
11. H. A. J. Gus Hedderburn
12. Calbert Best
13. Percy Paris
14. Senator Donald H. Oliver
15. Dr. Daurene Lewis, OC
16. Delmore Buddy Daye
17. Judge Linda Carvery
18. Mayann E. Francis
19. Gordon Earle
20. Graham Downey
21. Wayne Adams

22. Office of African Nova Scotian Affairs
23. Black Educators Association
24. Madame Justice Valerie Miller
25. Black Artist Network
26. Equity Lodge
27. Black Business Initiative
28. Beresford A. Husbands
29. Nova Scotia Home for Coloured Children
30. George Washington Carver Credit Union
31. Kwaacha House
32. Royal Canadian Mounted Police
33. Nova Scotia Association for the Advancement of Coloured People
34. Black Loyalist Heritage Society
35. Congress of Black Women of Canada Preston/ Cherry Brook/Lake Loon/Westphal & Area Chapter
36. the murder of Graham Cromwell
37. Fred Hodges
38. Henderson Paris
39. Mayann E. Francis
40. Concerned Citizens of Lincolnville
41. Kirk Johnson
42. Ruth Golar (left) and Connie Golar (right)

Sports

1. Cyril Fraser Jr.
2. Marjorie Turner
3. George E. Dixon
4. Ryan Williams
5. Frank Dorrington
6. Willie O'Ree
7. Robert Mark Smith
8. Wayne D. Smith
9. Robert Bobby Smith
10. Curtis Coward
11. Brooke Buckland
12. Regina Horne (Fraser)
13. Tyrone Williams
14. Brad Barton, OC
15. Dennie Oliver (former university star) and Derrico Wigginton (signed right out of high school)
16. Debbie Miller Brown
17. Denny Clyke, Joe Worrell, Billy Carter, Roy Mansfield
18. Cecil Wright
19. #1–Sam Langford (boxing), #4–George Dixon (boxing), #7–Clyde Gray (boxing), #10–Robert Mark Smith (softball/fast pitch)
20. Clobie Collins
21. Wayde Bowles, a.k.a. Rocky Johnson

22. front row: Irvine Lucas, Cortland Davis, George Skeir, George White, Charlie Smith, Lou Gannon Sr., Walter Skeir; back row: Jimmy Springer, Gordon Jemmett, Wilbur Izzie Izzard, Herbie Bruce, Alcid Nicholas, Doug Dawson, Wendell Skeir Sr., and the coach, Al McCullem; seated in front: bat boy/mascot Bobby Smith

23. Raymond Downey

24. Bill Riley

25. Stanley Chook Maxwell

26. Provincial Black Basketball Tournament

27. Manny MacIntyre (New Brunswick), Ossie Carnegie, and Herb Carnegie

28. Coloured Hockey League of the Maritimes

29. Joe Louis

30. John T. Jack Mills

31. This was the first time ever that all three game officials were African Nova Scotian. The officials for the game were Wendell Skeir, Calvin Headley, and Brian States.

32. Cindy Gill

Education, Literature, and Journalism

1. Shallyn Williams
2. Dr. Wanda Thomas Bernard
3. Dr. Adrienne Dorrington
4. African Canadian Services Division
5. Noel Johnston
6. Rev. Dr. William H. Golar
7. Madeline Symonds
8. Mary Matilda Winslow
9. The African School
10. James R. Johnston
11. William Gosman
12. *James Robinson Johnston: The Life, Death and Legacy of Nova Scotia's First Black Lawyer*
13. *Black Social Workers in Nova Scotia: Fighting for Change*
14. *Share and Care: The Story of the Nova Scotia Home for Coloured Children*
15. *Native Song*
16. *You Had Better Be White By Six A.M.: The African-Canadian Experience in the Royal Canadian Mounted Police*
17. *Black and Bluenose: The Contemporary History of a Community*
18. George Hector
19. Maxine Tynes
20. *Who's Who in Black Canada*
21. *A Lesson in Boxing*

22. Dr. A. Pearleen Oliver

23. Robert Upshaw

24. 1996

25. W. A. Spray

26. 2003

27. Dr. Bridglal Pachai

28. Donna Byard Sealey

29. David Downey

30. *Black Women Who Made a Difference in Nova Scotia*

31. *Images of Our Past: Historic Black Nova Scotia*

32. *Traditional Lifetime Stories: A Collection of Black Memories*

33. *Black Islanders*

34. *The Clarion*

35. Dr. Carrie Best Award

36. Sherri Borden-Colley

37. Wayne Adams, Mayann E. Francis, Joan Jones, Charles Saunders

38. Sheryl Grant

39. *The Atlantic Advocate*

40. Master of Education (Studies in Lifelong Learning) with a concentration in Africentric Leadership

41. *Nova Scotia Gleaner*

42. *Little Black Sambo*

43. Wade H. Smith

Military, Law, and Justice

1. Hartley Gosline
2. Superintendent R. G. Ted Upshaw, Three Miles Plains (first to be commissioned, 1999); Superintendent Craig Gibson, Gibson Woods (second to be commissioned, 2002); Inspector I. Tom Jones, Truro (third to be commissioned, 2005)
3. Yvonne Atwell
4. Auxiliary Constable Keith A. Miller, RCMP Yarmouth Town Detachment
5. Judge Corrine Sparks
6. Sergeant Leanne MacDonald
7. Constable A. Dean Simmonds
8. Alfred Coward and Leslie Bryan
9. Rose Fortune
10. No. 2 Construction Battalion
11. Maj. Dr. Marguerite A. Peggy Downes, OMM, CD
12. Sapper Percy Fenton
13. Thelma Coward Ince
14. William E. Hall, VC
15. Alexander Jackson, Arnold Johnson, Rev. Wrenfred Bryant, Arthur Downey, and Rev. Dr. Willard P. Clayton
16. Shawna Y. (Paris) Hoyte
17. Rick Smith
18. Allan Bundy

Arts and Culture

1. Charles R. Bucky Adams
2. Dr. George Elliott Clarke
3. Dr. Walter Borden
4. Edith (Drummond) Clayton and Clara Gough (daughter)
5. Dr. Sylvia Hamilton
6. Merril Bruce (East Green Harbour) and George Adams (Halifax)
7. Jeremiah Sparks
8. *Beatrice Chancey*
9. George Borden
10. George Boyd
11. Marko Simmonds
12. Lorne White (top) and David Wells (bottom)
13. African Nova Scotian Music Association
14. Ritchie Gray and James MacQuaid, a.k.a. MCJ and Cool G
15. Gary Beals
16. The original members were Sebert Kelly, Ernie Johnson, Gerald Francis, and Malcolm Berry. The additional members not pictured were Ed Fells and Charlie Smith.
17. Paddy Knight, Conrad Gordon, Herman Peterson, and Eldon Thomas
18. Portia White
19. Les Sykes

20. Clifton Davis
21. Clara Carvery-Adams
22. Jermaine Downey
23. Harold Cromwell

Business and Careers

1. Donna Guy
2. Michael Duck
3. Beverly Mascoll
4. Angela Johnson
5. Louis Gannon Jr.
6. Ruth Bailey and Gwen Barton
7. Jocelyn Dorrington
8. Charlie Carter
9. Dorothy Paris
10. Clotilda Yakimczuk
11. David Woods
12. Jeneen Williams
13. Tracey Jones

Religion

1. Cornwallis Street Baptist Church
2. 1854; Granville Mountain
3. Rev. Richard Preston
4. Rev. Elaine Walcott
5. Rev. Tracy Grosse
6. Rev. Dr. Peter J. Paris
7. Vera Clyke
8. Rev. David George

Achievements

1. Craig Cromwell
2. Dr. Marie Hamilton
3. Rev. Capt. Dr. William Andrew White
4. Dr. A. Pearleen Oliver
5. Laura Howe
6. Walter Bubby Peters
7. Ed Matawaana (humanitarian), Brooke Buckland (sports—youth), Moneta James (performing arts), and Cst. Craig M. Smith (community service)
8. Isaac Phils, OC
9. Evelina Upshaw
10. Veronica Marsman

Historical Events, Locations, and Places

1. Danny Glover
2. Gerrish Street Hall
3. Black Cultural Centre
4. Birchtown, Shelburne County
5. Halifax
6. Nova Scotia, New Brunswick, and Prince Edward Island
7. Maurice Reddick, a.k.a. The Singing Miner
8. The Black Cultural Centre of Nova Scotia and the Black Loyalist Heritage Society
9. The Arrows Club
10. Terry Symonds
11. Fortress Citadel, Citadel Hill
12. *Amistad*
13. Freetown
14. Africville Reunion
15. Olivier LeJeune
16. Black Sam's Bridge
17. Michaëlle Jean, Governor General of Canada (left), and Mayann E. Francis, Lieutenant-Governor of Nova Scotia (right)
18. The Victoria Jubilee Club
19. Rev. Dr. Martin Luther King Jr.

Common Demoninator

1. railroad workers
2. Canada Post employees
3. police officers
4. teachers
5. legal professionals
6. boxers
7. pageant queens
8. members of the clergy
9. bus drivers
10. nurses

Name the Date

1. 1993
2. 1952
3. August 1820
4. 1945
5. 1969
6. 1962
7. 1968
8. May 1995
9. 1800–1860
10. 1816
11. 1954
12. 1605
13. 1984
14. 1964
15. January 19, 1825
16. 1984; David Woods
17. 1982; Halifax's Lord Nelson Hotel

Name the Place

1. Truro, NS
2. New Glasgow, NS
3. Cape Breton, NS (Whitney Pier, Glace Bay, Stirling, New Waterford, Sydney)
4. Digby County, NS (Weymouth, Weymouth Falls, Southville)
5. Yarmouth County, NS (Greenville, Yarmouth)
6. Halifax County, NS (Cherry Brook, East Preston, North Preston)
7. Cumberland County, NS (Amherst, Springhill)
8. Halifax (Africville), NS
9. Digby County, NS (Digby, Jordantown, Acaciaville)
10. Shelburne, NS
11. Saint John, NB
12. Fredericton, NB
13. Halifax/Dartmouth, NS
14. Prince Edward Island

African Canadian Icons

1. Angela James (Ontario)
2. John Ware (Alberta)
3. Elijah McCoy (Ontario)
4. William Sylvester Adolphus Beal (Manitoba)
5. Mifflin Gibbs (British Columbia)
6. Rueben Mayes (Saskatchewan)
7. Portia White (Nova Scotia) and Oscar Peterson (Quebec). Peterson was the first living Canadian to be so honoured.
8. Marie-Joseph Angélique (Quebec)

Who am I?

1. Dr. Carrie Best
2. Edward Mitchell Bannister
3. Charlie Ryan
4. Gordon Earle
5. Measha Brueggergosman
6. Shauntay Grant
7. George Budge Byers

Acknowledgements

I would like to thank the following individuals and organizations for their support: Sharon Robart-Johnson, Ernest Johnson, Bruce Johnson, South West Regional Library (Yarmouth), Black Loyalist Heritage Society, Randy Fells, Joan Jones, Dr. Jim Hornby, Dr. Bridglal Pachai, Madame Justice Valerie Miller, Office of the Lieutenant Governor of Nova Scotia, Halifax North Memorial Public Library, Art Gallery of Nova Scotia, Sylvia Hamilton, George Fosty, Beverly Connolly, CBC, Tracy Thomas, Vivian Dixon, Lou Gannon Sr., Lou Gannon Jr., Dr. Leslie Oliver, Mr. Herb Carnegie, Dr. Peter J. Paris, Future Aces Foundation, Nova Scotia Public Archives, David Woods, Royal Canadian Mounted Police, Juanita Peters, Bernice Carnegie, African Nova Scotian Music Association, Hank Snow Museum, Howie Spears, Black Cultural Centre, Dr. Henry Bishop, Russell Grosse, Cecil Wright, Barry States, B. A. Husbands Photo Collection, Office of African Nova Scotian Affairs, Prince Edward Island Sports Hall of Fame, Brayona Downey, Jamera Berry, Dyrekia Provo, Jelilah Provo, and the staff at Nimbus. Special thank-you's go to Tracey Jones for suggesting me for this project and to Rosella Fraser for taking the time to review my material.

A few years ago while watching *Jeopardy!* my two beautiful daughters dubbed me "Mr. Useless Facts." Hopefully this book helps to dispel that myth.

Bibliography

Alexander, Ken and Avis Glaze. *Towards Freedom: The African-Canadian Experience*. Toronto: Umbrella Press, 1996.

Anderson, Ricky. *Win in the Arena of Life: Living a Life You Love Is Worth Fighting For*. Fairfield, CT: Aslan, 2003.

Ashe, Robert. *Halifax Champion: Black Power in Gloves*. Halifax: Formac, 2006.

Bernard, Wanda Thomas, ed. *Fighting for Change: Black Social Workers in Nova Scotia*. Lawrencetown, NS: Pottersfield, 2006.

Borden, Sherri. "Black men's group to fight sentences given in Watt's case." *Halifax Chronicle Herald*, August 7, 1999.

Brewster, Murray. "RCMP entrance exam modified in light of federal equity report." *Halifax Chronicle Herald*, February 24, 1998.

Brooks, Patricia. "Halifax's first black sergeant 'challenged everything.'" *Halifax Chronicle Herald*, May 12, 1999.

Brooks, Patricia. "Officer says hello via satellite feed, students chat with first NS Mountie." *Halifax Daily News*, January 16, 1995.

Clarke, George Elliott. *Execution Poems*. Kentville, NS: Gaspereau, 2001.

Clarke, George Elliott. "The Birmingham of Nova Scotia: The Weymouth Falls Justice Committee vs. the Attorney General of Nova Scotia." *The New Maritimes*. Dec. 1986–Jan. 1987.

Coward, Curtis and Tony Seed. *The Kid's Baseball Book: An Autobiographical Guide for Canadian Youth and Coaches*. Halifax: New Media Services, 1994.

Evans, Doris and Gertrude Tynes. *Telling the Truth: Reflections: Segregated Schools in Nova Scotia*. Dartmouth, NS: Association of Retired School Teachers, 1995.

Ffrench, Robert, Henry V. Bishop, ill., Susan Lucy, ed. *Out of the Past, Into the Future*. Toronto: Umbrella Press, 1994.

Fosty, George and Darril Fosty. *Black Ice: The Lost History of the Coloured Hockey League of the Maritimes 1895–1925*. New York: Stryker-Indigo, 2004.

Francis, Flora (Blizzard). *A Black Canadian Bibliography*. Ottawa: Pan-African Publications, 2000.

Grizzle, Stanley G. with John Cooper. *The Story of the Brotherhood of Sleeping Car Porters in Canada: My Name is Not George*. Toronto: Umbrella Press, 1998.

Holas, W. P. *Millennium Minds: 100 Black Canadians*. Toronto: Pan-African Publications, 2000.

Hornby, Jim. *The Black Islanders*. Charlottetown: Institute of Island Studies, 1991.

Johnston, Justin Marcus. *James Robinson Johnston: The Life, Death and Legacy of Nova Scotia's First Black Lawyer*. Halifax: Nimbus, 2005.

Jones, Randy. "Racism under arrest, NS Mountie first African Canadian to don red serge." *Halifax Chronicle Herald*, January 13, 2004.

Killiam, Crawford. *Go Do Some Great Things: The Black Pioneers of British Columbia*. Vancouver: Douglas & McIntyre, 1978.

Kimber, Stephen. "Monday Profile—Cpl. Calvin Lawrence." *Halifax Chronicle Herald*, May 28, 1996.

Medel, Brian. "NS Mountie brings black history to Florida youth." *Halifax Daily News*, March 25, 2002.

Nolan, Lynell. *Being Black in Scarlet*. Bloomington, IN: Authorhouse, 2003.

Nunn, Bruce. "The sticky details of our Aunt Jemima, NS woman portrayed syrup matron." *Globe and Mail*, January 14, 1995.

Oliver, A. Pearleen. *Song of the Spirit: An Historical Narrative On the History of the Beechville United Baptist Church 150th Anniversary*. Nova Scotia: Lancelot, 1994.

O'Ree, Willie and Michael McKinley. *The Autobiography of Willie O'Ree: Hockey's Black Pioneer*. Toronto: Sommerville House, 2000.

Pachai, Bridglal. *Beneath the Clouds of the Promised Land: The Survival of Nova Scotia's Blacks, Vol. 2, 1800–1989*. Halifax: Black Educators Association, 1990.

Pachai, Bridglal and Henry V. Bishop. *Images of Our Past: Historic Black Nova Scotia*. Halifax: Nimbus, 2006.

Power, Bill. "Reaching new heights, Upshaw makes RCMP history." *Halifax Chronicle Herald*, May 12, 1999.

Ruck, Calvin W. *The Black Battalion 1916–1920: Canada's Best Kept Secret*. Halifax: Nimbus, 1987.

Sadlier, Rosemary. *The Kids Book of Black Canadian History*. Toronto: Kids Can Press, 2003.

Saunders, Charles. *Black and Bluenose: The Contemporary History of a Community*. Lawrencetown, NS: Pottersfield, 1999.

Smith, Craig Marshall. *Journey: African Canadian Study Guide*. Yarmouth, NS: C. M. S. Publishing, 2000.

Smith, Craig Marshall. *You Had Better Be White By Six A. M.: The African-Canadian Experience in the Royal Canadian Mounted Police*. Yarmouth, NS: C. M. S. Publishing, 2006.

Spray, W. A. *The Blacks in New Brunswick*. Fredericton, NB: Brunswick Press, 1972.

Story, Alan. "In jury urged into remarks about blacks by N.S. judge." *Toronto Star*, January 7, 1986.

Thomson, Colin A. *Born With a Call: A Biography of Dr. William Pearly Oliver, CM*. Cherry Brook, NS: Black Cultural Centre for Nova Scotia, 1986.

Tynes, Maxine. *Borrowed Beauty*. Lawrencetown, NS: Pottersfield, 1987.

Williams, Dawn. *Who's Who in Black Canada: Black Success and Black Excellence in Canada, A Contemporary Directory*. Toronto: D. P. Williams & Associates, 2002.

Williams, Dolly, ed. *Black Women Who Made a Difference in Nova Scotia*, vol. 1. East Preston, NS: Congress of Black Women of Canada (Preston/Cherry Brook/ Lake Loon/Westphal and Area Chapter), 2007.

Woods, David. *Native Song*. Lawrencetown, NS: Pottersfield, 1990.

A variety of assistance and material was supplied by:

Halifax North Memorial Public Library, Black History Vertical File, 2285 Gottingen St., Halifax, Nova Scotia

Halifax Regional Library Information Services, Spring Garden Road Memorial Public Library, 5381 Spring Garden Rd., Halifax, Nova Scotia

Black Cultural Centre of Nova Scotia, 1149 Main St., Dartmouth, Nova Scotia

Image Sources

Organizations, Politics, and Social Justice

Question 6: courtesy of Craig Marshall Smith

Question 17: courtesy of Barry States and the B. A. Husbands Halifax Coloured Citizens Improvement League Collection

Question 24: courtesy of Madame Justice Valerie Miller

Question 26: courtesy of Bobby Smith

Question 33: courtesy of the Black Cultural Centre of Nova Scotia

Question 39: courtesy of the office of the Lieutenant-Governor of Nova Scotia

Question 42: courtesy of Barry States and the B. A. Husbands Halifax Coloured Citizens Improvement League Collection

Sports

Question 12: courtesy of the Black Cultural Centre of Nova Scotia

Question 17: courtesy of Howie Spears

Question 22: courtesy of Lou Gannon Sr.

Question 27: courtesy of the Future Ace Foundation

Education, Literature, and Journalism

Question 5: courtesy of the Black Cultural Centre of Nova Scotia

Question 21: courtesy of Halifax Public Libraries—Information Services Department

Question 39: courtesy of Nova Scotia Archives and Records Management

Military, Law, and Justice

Question 4: courtesy of the Yarmouth Vanguard

Question 17: courtesy of Jahalia Smith

Arts and Culture

Question 1: courtesy of the African Nova Scotia Music Association

Question 5: courtesy of Dr. Sylvia Hamilton

Question 12: courtesy of the Canadian Broadcasting Corporation

Question 14: courtesy of James McQuaid

Question 16: courtesy of Sharon Robart-Johnson

Question 22: courtesy of the Black Cultural Centre of Nova Scotia

Question 23: collection of the Art Gallery of Nova Scotia. Gift of Chris Huntington, Mahone Bay, Nova Scotia, 1993.

Business and Careers

Question 9: courtesy of Vivian Dixon and Tracy Thomas

Religion

Question 6: courtesy of Princeton University

Historical Events, Locations, and Places

Question 9: courtesy of the Halifax North Memorial
Public Library

Question 17: courtesy of Shirley Robb

Who am I?

Question 2: collection of the Art Gallery of Nova Scotia.
Purchased with funds provided by Sheldon and
Marjorie Fountain, 2006.

Question 6: courtesy of Rosella Fraser

Question 7: courtesy of the Prince Edward Island Sports
Hall of Fame